GW00674957

THIS

Balamory

ANNUAL

BELONGS TO

. . . .

Balamory

BBC

ANNUAL 2006

RED FOX

GET TO KNOW MISS HOOLIE

Hi there, how are you? Do you know who I am? That's right, I'm Miss Hoolie, I live in the green house and I run the Balamory Nursery. I spend lots of time at the Nursery and the children and I have great fun splodging, sticking, dancing, listening to stories and singing.

My Balamory friends are always popping in to say hello and help with storytime or activities – the children and I love that!

Today is a work day; everyone is at work and school and I am at the Nursery – it's lovely and sunny today. On play days I am out and about, whatever the weather!

Fun and games

Sandpit fun!

Storytime

MISS HOOLIE FACTFILE

Born	On a Monday – Fair of Face
Colour of eyes	Sea blue
Favourite book	*Alice in Wonderland* by Lewis Carroll
Favourite food	Italian Food, Lasagne
Favourite song	"Oh My Darlin' Clementine" and "She'll Be Coming Round the Mountain"
Favourite animal	Cat
Favourite day out	Sailing
Hobby	Gardening
Family	Miss Hoolie's mum and dad live in the Big City, her brother Hamish is a scuba diver and he has two children, Miss Hoolie's niece and nephew, Clara and Jack.
Funny holiday story	Miss Hoolie and Edie went to Iceland to look for the Snow Flake Fairy. It was brilliant fun and a great adventure seeing all the glaciers and it was funny when the geyser suddenly blew steam up into the air.
Don't like	Don't tell, but Miss Hoolie is more than a little frightened of spiders
Habit	No one knows this, but Miss Hoolie is quite messy at home!

MISS HOOLIE'S BALAMORY ABC

Today is a work day in Balamory – let's practise our ABC – it's as easy as 1, 2, 3, ask Penny! What other words can you think of beginning with each letter?

Archie

Bicycle

Cup

Duster

Edie

Ferry

Green

Hula Hoop

Inventions

Josie

Kilt

Ladder

Mm — Miss Hoolie

Nn — Nobby

Oo — Orange

Pp — Penny, PC Plum

Qq — Quilt

Rr — Rocket

Ss — Spencer, Suzie

Tt — Ted

Uu — Umbrella

Vv — Violin

Ww — Whale

Xx — Xylophone

Yy — Yoghurt pot

Zz — Zebra crossing

Now everybody, again from the top!
Practising your Balamory ABC is fun!

9

GET TO KNOW EDIE McCREDIE

Oh, hello. You've caught me on the hop today, I'm in the middle of fixing something . . . Aha, there we go – as good as new. I'm sure you know me . . . that's right, I'm Edie McCredie and I drive the daisy bus. I live in a cosy little place in the blue house, just above the bus garage. As you have probably noticed, I'm rather good at fixing things, so all my Balamory friends find me very useful! Give me a spanner and I'll mend anything. What I really love is driving around town to see my friends and travelling farther afield. I've been all over the world and had lots of adventures – oh, boy, have I got some stories to tell . . . You should come and see my videos some time . . .

Where would you like to go?

Parp parp!

EDIE'S TOP TRAVEL TIPS:

- Always be prepared
- Take a spanner everywhere you go – you never know when it might come in handy!
- Always be ready for new adventures
- Never annoy a camel – they can be very bad tempered!
- Video everything so you can share your adventures with all your friends

Let's find the way

EDIE McCREDIE FACTFILE

Born — On a Thursday – Far to Go

Colour of eyes — Bluey grey

Favourite book — *Around the World in 80 Days* by Jules Verne

Favourite food — Thai Food

Favourite song — "Frère Jacques"

Favourite animal — Camel – even if they can be a bit grumpy!

Favourite day out — Driving around Balamory waving hello to all her friends

Hobby — Metal work and exploring new places with her video camera

Family — Edie's mum lives in Cornwall

Funny holiday story — Edie spent a week living with the gorillas in the Congo – what an experience!

Don't like — Edie gets very cross with bad driving – road safety is very important to her

Habit — You've probably noticed this already, but Edie can't sit still – she always has to be doing something, whether it's fixing things, editing videos, tidying her house or just generally rushing around

11

FRANCE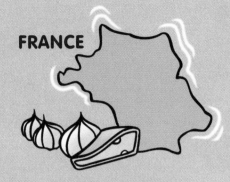

SPAIN

EGYPT

AROUND THE WORLD

HOLLAND

WITH EDIE McCREDIE

I've seen lots of exotic and exciting things on my travels. See whether you can match the items on the opposite page to the countries they come from.

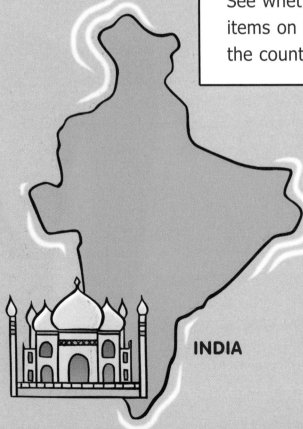

INDIA

AUSTRALIA

GET TO KNOW ARCHIE (AND NOBBY)

Oh, hello there . . . Hang on a minute, you've just caught me in the middle of something – sorry! Ah, that's better. Right, well, welcome to my castle. I'm Archie and this over here is Nobby, my robot.

I am an inventor and I live up at the pink castle. I am always collecting bits and bobs around Balamory that come in awfully handy with my inventions. Just look at this. Can you guess what it's made from? That's right . . . yoghurt pots, buttons and bits of string.

Archie's pink castle

Here are some of my other inventions. Splendid, aren't they – it is amazing what you can make from the things people throw away! Why don't you try inventing too?

Clip-clop puppet

Carting with Plummers

Yoghurt pot telephone

ARCHIE FACTFILE

Born On a Friday – Loving and Giving

Colour of eyes Blue

Favourite book *The Time Machine* by H. G. Wells

Favourite food Yoghurt

Favourite song "Ging Gang Goolie"

Favourite animal Osprey

Favourite day out The Science Museum

Hobby Inventing absolutely anything!

Family Archie has a big family, including three nephews, Alec, Andy and Christopher, a cousin Jeremy, an uncle Barney and his great-aunt Poppy, who loves hang-gliding!

Funny holiday story Archie had a marvellous time when he visited Paris to taste the local yoghurt and collect cartons. He even made an Eiffel Tower out of yoghurt pots!

Don't like Archie doesn't like waste at all – if everything was thrown away, what would he create his wonderful inventions from?

Habit Archie NEVER throws anything out – you never know when it might come in handy

MAKE YOGHURT POT TELEPHONES!

You won't believe it, but you can make a splendid telephone with just some string and two old yoghurt pots – here's how . . .

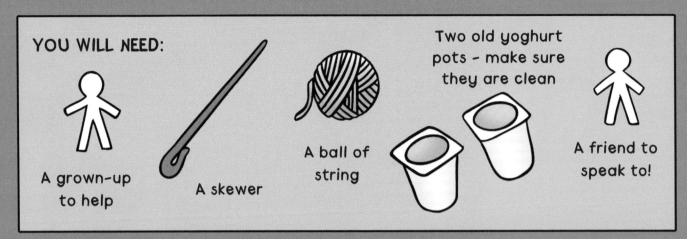

YOU WILL NEED:

A grown-up to help

A skewer

A ball of string

Two old yoghurt pots - make sure they are clean

A friend to speak to!

HOW TO MAKE ARCHIE'S YOGHURT POT TELEPHONES:

1 Ask a grown-up to help you make a small hole in the bottom of each yoghurt pot using the skewer.

2 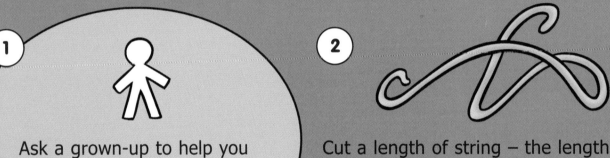 Cut a length of string – the length depends on how far away you and your telephone buddy want to be. Try 3–4 metres to start with.

3  Thread the string through the holes in the yoghurt pots and ask a grown-up to help you tie a big knot on the inside of the yoghurt pot so that the string is secure.

4 And there you have it, your yoghurt pot telephone!

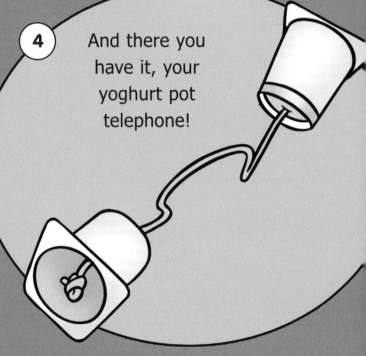

HOW TO USE ARCHIE'S YOGHURT POT TELEPHONES:

Your friend should hold their yoghurt pot to their ear while you speak into your yoghurt pot, then swap over and listen as your friend talks to you through the yoghurt pot telephone. You can chat like this for as long as you like – why not try it with one of you inside and the other outside by threading the string through an open window . . .

REMEMBER, THIS WILL ONLY WORK IF THE STRING IS TIGHT

YOUR VOICE IS CARRIED ALONG THE STRING BY VIBRATIONS!

ARCHIE'S TOP TEN INVENTIONS

Yoghurt Pot Telephones
Rocket
Crazy Clip-clop Puppet
Carrot Picker
Puppet Show Television
Jam-spreading Machine
Sing-a-long Machine
Hear Me Hat
Yoghurt Pot Bird
Musical Hamper

Get yoghurt-potting!

GET TO KNOW JOSIE JUMP

Hey there! How are you today? I am always full of energy, I just can't sit still. You know who I am, don't you? That's right . . . I'm Josie Jump and I live in the yellow house. I am the Balamory Fitness Instructor. I love what I do because it means I can do sport all day long if I want to. Sometimes I just stay at home, jump on my trampoline and listen to music and dance, but it's great to get out and about, jogging around Balamory and seeing all my friends, and I do love a trip to see the ballet.

I like to know what the story is in Balamory, so I often pop into Pocket and Sweet's for a gossip and I love going to the Nursery to tell the children stories. Storytelling is great fun, especially making up actions to help tell the story . . .

Jogging round Balamory

Gossiping with Suzie

18

JOSIE JUMP FACTFILE

Born — On a Tuesday – Full of Grace

Colour of eyes — Brown

Favourite book — *Little Miss Tickle* by Roger Hargreaves

Favourite food — Beans on toast

Favourite song — "Heads, Shoulders Knees and Toes"

Favourite animal — Gazelle

Favourite day out — Josie loves to jog around Balamory and wave to her friends

Hobby — Playing rugby

Family — Josie has a sister, Jane, who is an airline pilot

Funny holiday story — Trip away cycling with the Tour de France . . . Josie had a great time

Don't like — You don't need to be told, as it is so obvious, but Josie hates sitting still!

Habit — Josie often falls asleep after exercising!

EXERCISE WITH JOSIE JUMP

Hi, everyone! I'm Josie Jump. I am so full of energy all the time that sometimes I just don't know what to do with it – the best way to burn it off is with a good stint of exercise, maybe you could help me . . . I love running, jumping, dancing and hula hooping – come on, let's get to it!

1 Put some funky tunes on the stereo and warm up with some gentle stretching

2 Run round your room or around your garden a couple of times . . . and stretch

3 And now for my favourite bit – jumping! (If you don't have a trampoline, you can always jump about on your bed but make sure you ask an adult first!) Then relax and stretch.

4 Boogie, woogie, dance to your favourite tune – sing along as well . . . then relax and stretch.

5 Hoop the hula hoop! How many times can you do it? If you don't have a hula hoop, try skipping or bouncing a football.

See ya, and keep jumping!

6 And stretch and relax – workout over. Wasn't that brilliant? Now I could do with a nice cup of tea – I wonder who will have one for me . . . that's right, Suzie Sweet. Bye!

GET TO KNOW SUZIE SWEET

Hello, today's a play day in Balamory so everyone is out and about and the café is really busy. How about a nice cup of tea and a piece of cake or a slice of quiche? Mmm, lovely! Just the thing to warm you up on a cold day.

I'm Suzie Sweet and I live in the red house with my friend Penny Pocket. Together we run the Balamory shop and café. Penny is a star at sums, so I leave that bit to her. I bake all the cakes for the café and I'm a dab hand at sales and dusting too! It's great to chat to all the people who pop in – I always know all the Balamory gossip!

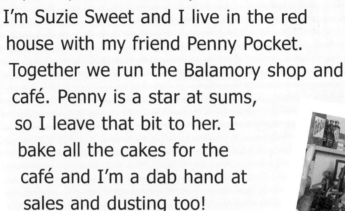

Pocket and Sweet's

Chatting on the phone

SUZIE SWEET'S TOP TEN TEATIME TREATS

Suzie and Penny

Apple Pie
Fish Cakes
Fruit Salad
Balamory Buns
Baked Potatoes
Custard Pies with Raspberries
Blueberry Muffins
Balamory Risotto
Chocolate Brownies
Spinach Quiche

SUZIE SWEET FACTFILE

Born — On a Saturday – Works Hard for a Living

Colour of eyes — Hazel

Favourite book — *Cooking with Keith Floyd* (he's Suzie's hero!)

Favourite food — Meatballs and Balamory Buns

Favourite song — "Shortnin' Bread"

Favourite animal — Budgies

Favourite day out — Flying

Hobby — Cooking

Family — Suzie has an aunt in Caithness on the mainland called Beatrice Brontë – Aunty B!

Funny holiday story — Suzie planned a trip to John O'Groats but ended up at Land's End!

Don't like — Suzie doesn't like it if she can't get someone something they want in the shop – she always likes to be able to get everything that her Balamory friends want or need.

Habit — Suzie is very affectionate and friendly to everyone.

SUZIE'S SULTANA BALAMORY BUNS

Hello, poppet. Let's make a teatime treat!

YOU WILL NEED:

A grown-up to help

1 egg

15g fresh yeast

clear honey

40g butter

100ml milk (at room temperature)

a pinch of salt

50g light brown soft sugar

100g sultanas

225g strong white flour

HOW TO MAKE 12 BALAMORY BUNS

1. Mix the yeast into the milk. Then, crack the egg into a small bowl and beat it.

2. Put the flour and the salt in a big bowl. Add 25g of the butter and use your fingers to rub it through the flour until the mixture looks like breadcrumbs. Make a hole in the middle and pour in the yeasty milk and the beaten egg. Use a wooden spoon to beat the mixture into a firm dough.

3. Ask an adult to show you how to knead the dough on a clean worktop sprinkled with flour. You should do this for 10 minutes until it is smooth and stretchy. Put the dough into a greased bowl and cover it with a damp tea towel. Leave it

in a warm place for about an hour and the yeast will make it rise until it is twice as big!

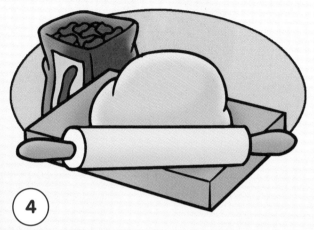

4

Now, knead the dough a little more, but softly this time. Roll it out with a rolling pin to make a rectangle about 30 x 23cm. Ask an adult to help you melt the rest of the butter, then brush this over the dough. Mix the sultanas and the brown sugar in a bowl, then sprinkle the mixture over the dough, making sure you leave 3cm of clear dough round all the edges.

You can try other fillings using any dried fruit you like instead of sultanas — why not make Archie's Apricot Buns, or PC Plum's Prune Buns? The recipe is the same, just ask an adult to chop the dried apricots or prunes into small pieces before you start.

 5

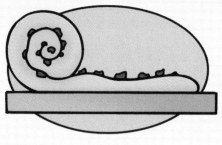

Now comes a tricky bit. Use the long edge to roll up the dough like a Swiss roll. Press firmly along the edge to stick it down, then ask an adult to cut the roll into 12 slices. Put them onto a greased baking tray and cover with a damp tea towel. Leave the tray in a warm place for half an hour and the slices will double in size again so make sure you leave plenty of space between them. Ask a grown-up to heat the oven to 190°C/375°F/gas mark 5.

 6

Ask an adult to put the Balamory Buns in the oven for half an hour – they should come out golden brown and nicely risen. Carefully brush the tops with a bit of honey while they are hot, then leave them to cool a little in the tin. Serve them while they are still warm –

delicious!

GET TO KNOW PC PLUM

Oh, hello there. How are you? It's already been quite a hectic day at Balamory Police Station – the phone hasn't stopped ringing all morning – I've hardly even had time for a cup of tea and a biscuit!

Having tea with friends

I'm PC Plum and I live in the white house. I expect you can tell from my uniform that I'm a policeman.

It's all go with this job as there's always something happening in Balamory.

I spend lots of time cycling around town looking for clues and solving mysteries. I solved the puzzle of the lost cow, helped Edie track down the missing scarecrow – that was a bit embarrassing actually, so enough of that – and found the beach litter bug, which was actually an otter! And, if you want to know anything about nature, I'm your man – just ask for PC Plum.

PC PLUM'S TOP DETECTION TIPS

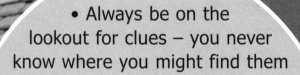

- Always be on the lookout for clues – you never know where you might find them

- Take a magnifying glass with you wherever you go

- Always have a notebook and pencil at the ready

- Ask lots of questions

- When following footprints, make sure they're not your own!

PC PLUM FACTFILE

Born On a Friday – Loving and Giving

Colour of eyes Bluey brown – PC Plum is very unusual!

Favourite book *The Adventures of Sherlock Holmes* by Sir Arthur Conan Doyle

Favourite food Spaghetti

Favourite song The songs from the opera, *Carmen* and "Ally Bally Bee"

Favourite animal PC Plum loves all animals – even creepy crawlies and beasties!

Favourite day out Sailing and any activity that he can do outside

Hobby Nature Trails and History

Family PC Plum's mum lives on Abbey Island – he loves going to visit her there

Funny holiday story PC Plum had a great time in Venice when he went with a policeman friend of his to find out how the Italian police work. They travelled everywhere by boat

Don't like Litter louts

Habit Drinking tea and eating biscuits – but he is trying to cut out sugar!

LOOKING FOR CLUES WITH PC PLUM

"Oh, PC Plum, there's a terrible racket in Balamory today – do you know who is making all that noise? I can't get a moment's peace."

beep beep!   Boing!   Miaow

Help PC Plum find out who is making all the noise. Draw a line to match the noise to where it is coming from and help PC Plum solve the mystery.

Oh dear, it seems everyone in Balamory is being noisy today – even the animals!

Clip-Clop

♪ ♪ ♪ ♪ ♪

WOof!

Answers: Beep Beep is coming from the Daisy Bus; Boing is coming from Josie's trampoline; Miaow is coming from Ted the cat; Clip-clop is coming from Archie's puppet; the music is coming from Spencer's guitar; Woof is coming from the dog

GET TO KNOW SPENCER

Hi there! How's tricks?
I'm Spencer and I just love to jazz things up
a little with my music and my paintbrushes.
Check out my handiwork in Balamory Harbour!
Funky colours, huh?

The different coloured houses of Balamory

I love to paint pictures too
and I cycle around Balamory
with my special trailer full of
painting gear so I can draw
and paint wherever I go.
Back at home I make funky
music with my
guitar and
saxophone, and
I make musical instruments from whatever I can
find – paint pots and saucepans can make
fab music! What can
you find to play?

My trailer

Making music

SPENCER FACTFILE

Born — On a Saturday – Works Hard for a Living

Colour of eyes — Brown

Favourite book — Books about Jackson Pollock and Picasso

Favourite food — Olives and Cheese

Favourite song — All jazz music

Favourite animal — Puffins

Favourite day out — A trip to the mainland to the Museum of Modern Art

Hobby — Making music with various homemade instruments

Family — Spencer's nephew, Calum, lives in Balamory and goes to the Nursery. He also has cousins, Max and Reagan, and a niece, Lucy

Funny holiday story — Spencer had a great time in Spain learning how to do the Flamenco dance!

Don't like — Washing up the paintbrushes after a day painting, but he knows it has to be done, or they can never be used again

Habit — Spencer is always tapping out rhythms on the table

SPENCER'S FUNKY FACE PAINTING

You can be whatever you want to be with my cool and funky face paints! From a wild lion, a sad clown, a cute little pussycat and a beautiful butterfly to a ferocious tiger – roooaaar!

I'll show you how to transform yourself into a TIGER – this will help you work out how to become many more amazing creatures!

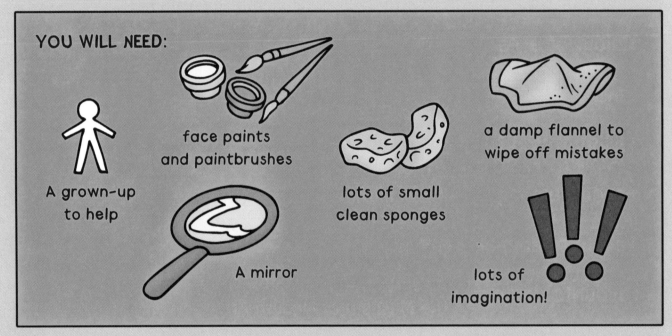

YOU WILL NEED:

A grown-up to help

face paints and paintbrushes

A mirror

lots of small clean sponges

a damp flannel to wipe off mistakes

lots of imagination!

Paints:
black, white, yellow, orange

1

Paint a white area around your mouth with a sponge.

2 Take a clean sponge and paint yellow around your eyes, on your cheeks and chin. With another sponge put orange paint around the edge of your face and down your nose. Blend the orange and yellow paints together at the edges with a sponge.

3

Paint eyebrows and whiskers in white with a medium-sized paintbrush. With black paint, add your tiger nose, black tiger stripes and paint your lips black.

4 Take a thin paintbrush and add black dots under your nose and outline your whiskers, eyes and eyebrows for a really wild tiger face!

Grrrrrrrr!

You can try other animals as well – like this butterfly – or make up your own!

BE CAREFUL NOT TO GET FACE PAINT IN YOUR EYES – IF YOU DO, TELL A GROWN-UP STRAIGHT AWAY

GET TO KNOW PENNY POCKET

Good morning! And how are you today?

I'm Penny Pocket and I run the shop and café with my friend Suzie Sweet. I expect she's already told you where we live . . . that's right, the red house. We work together in the shop, but I leave all the cooking for the café to Suzie – she's a real whiz in the kitchen. I stick to my speciality – organizing things and thinking of new ideas to make the shop run more smoothly. I love to count the money at the end of the day because numbers are my thing. I think numbers are cool.

When I have time off I love to go and watch my favourite football team, Castle United. I get lots of tips on how to referee for the five-a-side team and the basketball team.

I like to make sure that all the Nursery school children eat healthily so I arrange daily deliveries to Miss Hoolie of crunchy green apples, juicy oranges and bright yellow bananas.

Pocket and Sweet's

With Suzie in the shop

With my calculator

PENNY POCKET FACTFILE

Born
On a Sunday – Bonny and Blithe, Good and Gay

Colour of eyes
Brown

Favourite book
Books on Egyptian History

Favourite food
Smorgasbord

Favourite song
"Where Is the Love" – The Black Eyed Peas

Favourite animal
St Bernard Dog

Favourite day out
Go-Karting

Hobby
Penny is the Rowing Club Coach

Family
Penny has a brother, Peter, in Newcastle – he is a headteacher at a school

Funny holiday story
Her best holiday ever was a shopping trip to the Continent with Suzie Sweet

Don't like
Waiting for things – Penny likes to get things done

Habit
Penny NEVER misses her favourite TV show – soap opera *Round and About*

35

SHOPPING!

"Morning, Josie, what brings you to the on this lovely

 day?" asks Penny.

"Hi, Penny, well since it is such a great day, Miss Hoolie and I thought

we would take the children to the  for a

and games. I am missing a few things, and I thought you might

be able to help: a and a ; oh, and a , so that we

can build a . Miss Hoolie made some 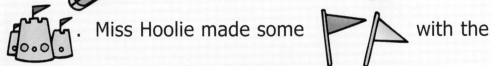 with the

 at the Nursery, so we can use these to decorate it.

I've got a , but we'll need a to sit on – I don't

want to get too sandy! And I think that's it," says Josie.

"But what about the food, Josie?" asks Penny.

"Oh, silly me – I forgot all about that!" laughs Josie.

"How about 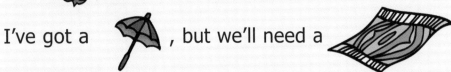 , a for everyone to share, some

and and some , " Penny suggests.

"Great, thanks, Penny, do you have all that stuff?" asks Josie.

"Can you help me find it . . .?" says Penny.

Help Penny and Josie get all the things they will need for the picnic. Look at the picture on the facing page, find everything, and circle it for them.

GRID DRAWING

Copy this picture of the daisy bus square
by square and then colour it in!

BAL MOR 1

BRIGHTEN THINGS UP!

Colour in the Balamory houses. Can you work out who lives where?

Pink

Yellow

Red

Pocket and Sweet

41

PARTY TIME!

Oh, hi there. How are you? Today is a work day in Balamory, but look what I've just found in my cupboard.

Gosh, this reminds me of all the brilliant parties we had when I was a wee girl.

42

Do you hear that? Here are the children now, and I think we've got a visitor . . . It's Josie!

"Hi, Miss Hoolie, what's that you've got?" asks Josie.

"Oh, this? It's a party toy I just found in the cupboard," Miss Hoolie replies.

"That's funny," says Josie, "I was going to suggest we do something really fun today. Why don't we have a For-No-Reason-At-All Party?"

"That's a great idea, Josie, but I haven't got the time to organize it," says Miss Hoolie.

"Leave it to me, I'll get this show on the road before you can say 'jelly and ice-cream!'"

Josie gets planning. "Right . . . games first. We want something with a bit of action and adventure. I know – a treasure hunt! But I'll be too busy organizing everything else to arrange this. I need someone to help and I know just the person. Edie McCredie! See you later, Miss Hoolie," Josie says as she jogs off.

Which colour house is Josie going to first today?

That's right . . . the blue house.

"Hiya, Edie, how's it going?" asks Josie.

"Oh! Hi, Josie. I was just checking the sprockets on the bus. What can I do for you today?"

Josie explains about the party and the games. "I was hoping you could plan the treasure hunt for me," she says.

"No problem, Josie. I know just what to do. I'll hide the treasure and put out a trail of clues to lead the children to it. Hmmn, I'm not too good at clues though. I know, I'll ask PC Plum to help!" says Edie.

"That's a fab idea. I'll leave you to it – I've still got lots to do: food, party hats, music . . . See you at the Nursery later." Josie dashes off to Pocket and Sweet's shop, while Edie heads for the Police Station to see PC Plum.

"Morning, Josie," says Penny. "What's the story in Balamory today?"

"Hi there. We're having a For-No-Reason-At-All Party at the Nursery later – everyone's invited – but I still need to get a few things. Firstly, we'll need some food."

"Well I can help you with that," says Suzie. "What do you fancy? Cakes? Sandwiches? Biscuits?"

"Wow, thanks! They all look great. I tell you what, make it a surprise, Suzie!" says Josie. "I'm also after some party hats – do you have any, Penny?"

"Oh, Josie, I'm so sorry, we've completely run out – I've ordered more, but they haven't arrived yet," says Penny.

"Oh no! We can't have a party without party hats," sighs Josie.

"How about Archie?" suggests Penny. "He can make anything . . ."

"Great idea. I'll go there now," says Josie. "Thanks, Penny. See you both at the Nursery."

"Good morning, Josie," says Archie. "Whatever's the matter? You look awfully hot and bothered. Is it anything I can help with?"

"Well actually I think it might be," says Josie. She explains her party hat dilemma to Archie and tells him all about the For-No-Reason-At-All Party.

"Oh dear, now that is a problem, but I've got just the thing. All you need is a bit of string, some card or paper, scissors and sticky tape – it's easy peasy, just look!" says Archie.

"First take the paper and draw around a big plate. Carefully cut the circle out, fold it in half and then cut along the fold. This will be enough for two party hats.

"Hold the flat edges together to make a cone, and stick them with sticky tape. Hey presto, a party hat! Now make a small hole on each side of the hat and thread a piece of string through them. Tie the ends with a knot and there's a perfect chin strap!"

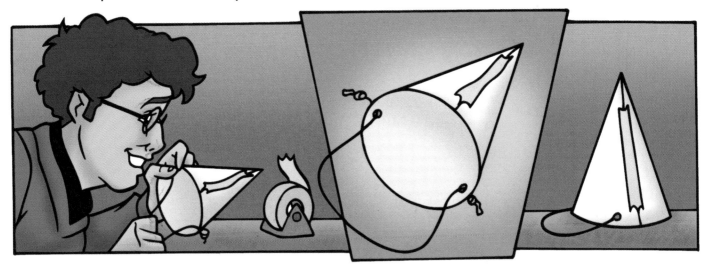

"Oh, Archie, you're a star! These hats are brilliant, but they are a bit plain," frowns Josie.

"Well how about we rustle up a few more and then go and see Spencer?" suggests Archie. "He's sure to be able to brighten them up!"

Archie and Josie get to it and make lots of hats in record time!

"Right – let's go to Spencer's right away," says Josie and she drags Archie out of the door.

"Hey, you guys, how's tricks?" says Spencer as Josie and Archie rush in with all the party hats. "Don't tell me, you're sorting things out for the big party this afternoon."

"How did you know?" asks Josie.

"Suzie and Penny told me all about it. I've already been over at the Nursery doing some face painting for the kids – they look wild!" grins Spencer. "Is there something else I can help with?"

"Well, since you ask, old chap, we were wondering if you could help us brighten up these party hats that we've made," says Archie.

"No problem – a splash of paint, some glitter and maybe even a feather or two – these are gonna look great!"

"Thanks, Spencer, that's brilliant," says Josie. "I'll leave you to it – I need to dash home to get my stereo – you can't have a party without music . . . see you there." Josie runs off towards the yellow house.

With Josie's music on the party really starts – Penny and Suzie have brought lots of tasty treats, the children's faces look fab, Edie and PC Plum's treasure hunt is great fun, even if some of the clues are a bit tricky, and Archie's party hats go down a storm.

"So, that was the story in Balamory today. Didn't everyone do a brilliant job, especially Josie? Would you believe it, PC Plum drank six cups of tea, and ate a few too many biscuits! It was a great party – I can't wait until the next one!"

51

WHO CAN HELP?

Some of your favourite Balamory friends need help – can you point them in the right direction? Draw a line to show who they should visit . . .

Miss Hoolie's cat Ted has climbed a great big tree, but he can't get down – poor Ted is stuck! Miaow! Who should Miss Hoolie call to help her get Ted down?

Suzie Sweet can't stop sneezing, and that is no good while she is working in the café and baking cakes! Who should Suzie go and see to make her feel better?

Spencer and Josie Jump are taking the children on an outing but they need to cross the road. Can you find someone to help them?

Poor old Archie has a terrible toothache! Who will be able to make him feel better?

Finlay the fireman

Lily the lollipop lady

Mr McGregor the dentist

Doctor Stewart

PC PLUM'S WORD PUZZLE

PC Plum is trying to find some words in this box of jumbled letters – can you help him?
Here are the words PC Plum is looking for – as soon as you find a word, draw a line through it and start looking for more!

CLUE ✓
TEAPOT ✓
MYSTERY ✓
ARCHIE ✓
BEETLE
JOSIE JUMP
CAKE ✗
SPENCER ✗
NURSERY ✗
BALAMORY ✗

B	E	E	T	L	E	B	A	P	C
J	A	I	T	D	M	N	Y	O	M
O	S	L	E	C	L	U	E	A	C
S	H	E	A	I	C	R	L	R	K
I	O	O	P	M	R	S	U	C	E
E	S	L	O	I	O	E	M	H	T
J	Z	I	T	E	P	R	R	R	I	S
U	E	E	K	D	N	Y	Y	E	W
M	S	A	Y	R	E	T	S	Y	M
P	C	W	S	P	E	N	C	E	R

SPOT THE DIFFERENCE

These two photographs appear the same, but if you look really carefully you'll see that there are 10 differences – can you find them all? When you find them, circle the differences on the bottom photo.

1

2

Answers from left to right: Beret on table; duster is pink; Balamory book on windowsill; "Pens" on pen-pot; watch on wrist missing; logo on jumper; spectacles are pink; orange screen on television; red wire coil missing; curtain tassel is yellow.

Bye, everyone!

We hope you enjoyed finding out a bit more about Balamory and had as much fun as we did with all the stories and the brilliant things to make and do!

See you next year!

BALAMORY COMPETITION!

bicycle

tricycle

Win a fabulous Balamory bicycle or tricycle

Win a brilliant Balamory DVD

Win a set of the latest Balamory books

All you have to do to win these fantastic prizes is answer this question:

What is the name of Miss Hoolie's cat?

The first correct entry will win all the prizes and the next 10 will win a DVD and a set of books. Send your answer on a postcard with your name and address to:

Balamory Annual 2006 Competition (JS)
Random House Children's Books
61–63 Uxbridge Road
London
W5 5SA

Remember to let us know if you'd prefer a Balamory bicycle or a Balamory tricycle if you win the main prize.

Terms and Conditions

The main prize is either a Balamory bicycle or a Balamory tricycle, plus a Balamory DVD and set of six Balamory books. Ten runners-up prizes are a Balamory DVD and a set of six Balamory books each.

The winner will be the first correct entry drawn at random from all the entries received by 28th February 2006.

The winner will be notified by 31st March 2006.

The competition is open to residents of the UK and Ireland. (Excluding employees of The Random House Group Ltd)

Only one entry per household.

No cash alternative.

No purchase necessary.

All entries must be received on a postcard or stuck-down envelope.

The judge's decision is final.

No correspondence will be entered into.

The Random House Group Ltd cannot accept any responsibility for entries which are lost or damaged in the post.

The Random House Group Ltd has arranged this competition in good faith but does not accept any liability relating to the prize. The Random House Group Ltd will use your personal info only for the purposes of this competition. Your personal details will not be kept on file by The Random House Group Ltd and they will not be passed on to third parties.

POLICE

There's something for every Balamory fan with this brilliant range of story and activity books.

Storybooks

Shaped Board Books

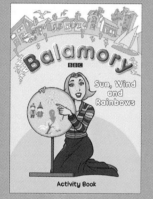 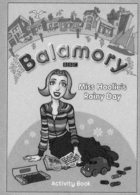

Colouring and Activity Books

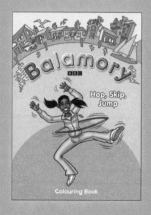 

 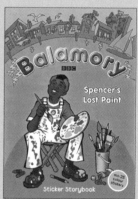

Sticker Books

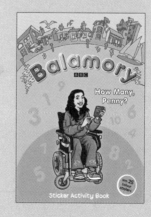 

And coming soon – magnetic storybooks with 9 shaped magnets and a playscene finale!

Look out for more exciting new books in the Balamory range throughout 2006

CONTENTS

page no.

6–7   Get to know Miss Hoolie

8–9   Miss Hoolie's Balamory ABC

10–11   Get to know Edie McCredie

12–13   Around the World with Edie McCredie

14–15   Get to know Archie (and Nobby)

16–17   Make Yoghurt Pot Telephones

18–19   Get to know Josie Jump

20–21   Exercise with Josie Jump

22–23   Get to know Suzie Sweet

24–25   Suzie's Sultana Balamory Buns

26–27   Get to know PC Plum

28–29   Looking for Clues with PC Plum